KU-037-583
This igloo book belongs to:

Contents

igloobooks

Published in 2019
by Igloo Books Ltd, Cottage Farm, Sywell, NN6 0BJ
www.igloobooks.com

Written by Melanie Joyce
Illustrated by Samantha Meredith

Designed by Justine Ablett
Edited by Stephanie Moss

REX001 1218
2 4 6 8 10 9 7 5 3 1
ISBN 978-1-78905-974-8

Printed and manufactured in China

Year Olds

igloobooks

Funtime Nursery
It was Charlie's first day at nursery and he had butterflies in his tummy.
You'll have fun,
said his mummy, smiling, but Charlie felt a bit upset.
I don't want to stay,
he said, his lip **wobbling**.

Then, a friendly voice
called his name.

Hello, Charlie.
We'll look after you,
don't worry,

said Miss Button,
the nursery teacher.

Miss Button introduced Charlie to the other children. They all smiled and said hello.

When it was time to play, Kaley and Tom came running up to Charlie.

Come on, we'll show you the dressing-up box!

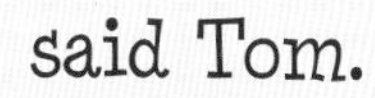

said Tom.

The box was full of all sorts of costumes. Charlie found a brilliant pirate hat and a big eyepatch.

I'm fierce Captain Charlie!

he cried.

Kaley and Tom **giggled.** They wanted to be pirates, too, so they pretended to sail out to sea, looking for adventure.

Kaley found some treasure, and and they even saw a sea monster!

There was lots of **noise** and **laughing** and **squealing.** Everyone at nursery was having so much fun.

After a snack and a drink, Kaley, Tom and Charlie did some painting.

said Kaley.

Charlie **laughed** because Kaley's picture looked really funny.

Next, Miss Button said they were going to play some music and sing a song.

Kaley **shook** a tambourine...

... Tom **tingled** a triangle...

... and Charlie

banged

a drum!

After all that noise, Miss Button said they could sit quietly in the book corner. Everyone settled down and she read a story about a little dragon who was afraid to fly.

Before long, Charlie saw Mummy at the door. He ran and **hugged** her. Then, he **waved** goodbye to Tom, Kaley and Miss Button.

The Wishing Wand

What if I found a **magic** wand, tucked right inside my pocket?
I'd wish that I could fly to space in a bright red, shiny rocket.

I'd make lots of cool, new alien friends
and I'd learn all of their names.
They'd say,
Welcome to our planet, Earthling,
then we'd play
lots of games.

After a while I'd invite
the aliens to come back
home with me.

I'd call Mummy and
Daddy to say,
I'll be home in
time for tea!

3, 2, 1
and...
... blast off!
We'd take off into space with
the engine booming.

We'd zip round planets and stars...
... and across the galaxy
we'd go zooming.

Back home we'd land in the garden.
The neighbours wouldn't believe their eyes.
Mummy and Daddy would **gasp** in amazement
at such an unexpected surprise.

My friends would think it was **fantastic**

that I brought aliens home to play.

We'd have a picnic together

and play games for the rest of the day.

At bedtime, the aliens would say,
Sorry, it's time to fly!
They'd **blast** off in the rocket, as I waved and said,
Goodbye!

When it was time to go to sleep, I'd put my magic wand away.
I'd snuggle up in bed and dream of the wishes I'd make the next day.

Best Ballet Friends

Bella longed to be a ballerina. One day, she saw Ginny and Ben practising ballet steps in Ben's garden, next door.

Rummaging in her dressing-up box, Bella pulled out a pair of Mum's old ballet shoes.

I can't wait to try these out in the garden!

she cried.

Bella **skipped** across the grass...

... and **leaped** into the air.

"I'm a ballerina!" she cried.

As Bella landed, she **skidded** on the grass and went **sliding** straight into the flower bed.

Jumping up, Bella pointed her toes and **twirled** round and round as fast as she could.

She spun dizzily out of control and landed with a

BUMP

in the vegetable patch.

So, Bella jumped straight up and **threw** her arms in the air, but she upset Mum's hanging basket and **tipped** flowers all over her head.

Ginny and Ben looked over the fence
and **rushed** down the garden path.

Bella sat down and told Ginny and Ben how much she wanted to learn to dance, just like them.

First, you point
your toes,

said Ginny.

Now step, then
one, two, three,

said Ben.

Then you hold
your arms up,

they said...

... turn and point,
then step, two, three!

cried Bella.

Ben and Ginny practised all afternoon with Bella and soon, she was doing all the steps perfectly. Ginny gave Bella one of her tutus and a nearly new pair of ballet shoes.

gasped Bella.

As Bella **whirled** and **twirled**, Mum was so impressed that she said Bella should have ballet lessons.
Thank you, Ginny and Ben. You're my best ballet friends,
said Bella.

Mucky Monsters

One day, Mum told Bess and Max that Auntie Jane was coming to visit.

asked Bess.

said Mum.

cried Max. He couldn't wait to dash outside into the sunshine.

First, Bess and Max played hide-and-seek, but Bess couldn't decide where to hide.

called Max.

Bess quickly **scrambled** under a bush, trying not to giggle.

Max looked everywhere for Bess, then suddenly he saw her.

he cried.

Bess **squealed** and rolled out onto the grass. Bits of leaves and dry twigs were stuck all over her!

But as Max tried to catch it, he got **tangled** up in the hose and **toppled** into the wheelbarrow.

Suddenly, the hosepipe **wriggled** like a snake and...
...swoosh!
Water shot out of the end, all over Bess.
I'm all wet! It's your fault, Max,
said Bess.

She chased her brother round the garden, until the two of them **slipped** and **slid** on the soggy grass.

Max **skidded** to a halt, just before the flower bed, but Bess was right behind him.

Max and Bess landed on the ground in a big soggy, grassy heap together, **sprinkled** all over with little flower petals.

Just then, Mum called from the kitchen to say that Auntie Jane had arrived. Max and Bess trudged inside, looking very dirty indeed.

They both said sorry to Mum for getting so messy.

said Mum, with a smile.

She looked at Auntie Jane, who burst out laughing.

said Auntie Jane, with a twinkle in her eye.

Sleep Tight, Bertie

It was night-time at Bertie's house and almost time for bed.

But Bertie didn't want to go to sleep.

Bertie told his mummy that when she switched off the light, he could hear noises and see things moving about in the night.

Mummy told him not to worry. It could be Night Owl in her tree.
She just loves staying up late, **hooting** as loudly as can be.

It might be kind
Mr Fox, **creeping**
back home in the
moonlight.

He's brought a surprise
for Mrs Fox, so he tries
to stay out of sight.

Maybe it's those naughty bunnies, all messing about next door.

They might be **bouncing** on their beds...

... or **rolling** around on the floor.

Mummy gave Bertie a hug and said,
There's no need to be afraid.
You just need to understand how
those funny noises are all made.

Bertie smiled and closed his eyes. He settled down without a peep.

He **snuggled** under the covers and fell into a happy sleep.